Knowing The Truth

2

KNOWING THE TRUTH

"*Jesus answered, 'I am the way and the truth and the life...'*"

JOHN 14:6

Operation Timothy

CBMC Publications

The Christian Business Men's Committee is an international evangelical organization of Christian business and professional men whose primary purpose is to present Jesus Christ as Savior and Lord to other business and professional men and to train these men to carry out the Great Commission.

CBMC of USA is a nondenominational, non-profit Christian ministry supported by gifts from people committed to reaching and discipling business and professional men for Jesus Christ.

More information may be obtained by writing:

Christian Business Men's Committee of USA
1800 McCallie Avenue
Chattanooga, Tennessee 37404
1-800-575-2262

Operation Timothy is an investigative Bible study with the goal of helping people to grow spiritually. It has been designed to serve as a link with the Living Proof I and II Video Series.
For more information, call 1-800-575-2262

Rob Suggs, *writer, cartoonist*

Isa Williams, *graphic designer*

Operation Timothy Workbook 1 – ISBN # 0-945292-02-3

Contents

APPOINTMENTS

Next Meeting _____ **Time** _____

_____

_____

_____

_____

Next Meeting _____ **Time** _____

_____

_____

_____

_____

Next Meeting _____ **Time** _____

_____

_____

_____

_____

Next Meeting _____ **Time** _____

_____

_____

_____

_____

Next Meeting _____ **Time** _____

_____

_____

_____

_____

Next Meeting _____ **Time** _____

_____

_____

_____

1 Gaining Eternal Assurance

That's What They Say:

Someone asked whether I ever worried about slipping through the Lord's fingers. I replied that it was impossible; you see, I am one of the fingers. By the new birth we become a part of the spiritual body of Christ. DONALD GREY BARNHOUSE

The world is a great sculptor's shop. We are the statues and there is a rumour going round the shop that some of us are some day going to come to life. C. S. LEWIS

WARM UP

Indiana Jones fights his way through scores of angry jungle villagers, scoundrels, and wild animals. Having entered the secret door to the ancient tomb, he puts his hands on the object of his quest: an invaluable jewel! But in a later struggle to escape, the jewel sinks into the quicksand — lost forever!

Having finally attained the jewel of salvation, can it be so easily lost? Can someone snatch it away? Or, can we lose our grip on it through simple indifference or loss of faith? These are troubling questions, but the Bible gives clear answers.

THE BIG PICTURE.

We'll deal with five issues in this section:

   I. The Source of Eternal Life
   II. Gaining Eternal Life
   III. Changed by Eternal Life
   IV. Assured of Eternal Life
   V. Eternal Life Now and Then

Getting Started

In Book I, *Finding the Way,* the Scripture references and verses were printed in the lesson. Beginning with Book II, you will need your own Bible to look up the references. The questions are based on the New International Version (NIV) translation of the Bible. If you don't have a Bible yet, please discuss this with your leader. Also, as a part of the lessons in Books II through IV, you will memorize a Scripture passage denoted at the end of each chapter.

I. THE SOURCE OF ETERNAL LIFE

Making the first move. When you want to hold a small child, who does the work? The child cannot climb up into your arms from the floor; but you can reach down and scoop her up. This is what God does for us. In the world's religions, people hold their arms heavenward and ask to be held. In Christianity, God picks us up.

According to 1 Peter 3:18, what is God's strategy for bringing us to Him?

Christ Died for our Sins

Read Luke 5:27-28. What does Jesus tell Levi (Matthew)? _Follow Me_

How does Levi respond? _Got up & Followed Jesus_

As you understand it, what do you think it means today to "follow" Jesus?

John 1:4 Who is the source of life? _Jesus is the Source of Life_

II. GAINING ETERNAL LIFE

"The Immaculate Reception." In football, that phrase recalls a famous, improbable touchdown pass. In a playoff game in the 1970's, the Pittsburgh Steelers were behind in the final seconds of the game. Terry Bradshaw, the Pittsburgh quarterback, threw a pass to his receiver, but the football bounced off an opposing player's back toward the line of scrimmage. Just before the ball hit the ground, Steelers' Franco Harris, ran up and snagged the deflected pass, running it into the end zone for the winning touchdown. But there's a far more improbable reception you and I can make. How do people like us receive the perfection and purity of Jesus?

a. John 1:12. Who can receive Him? _____*All*_____ How? _____

_____

b. Romans 10:9,10. What two actions are involved? _____
_____*Confess with Your Mouth — Believe in Your Heart*_____

Why is what we say — not just what we think — important?_____

_____

Don't look back. Wise old baseball player Satchel Paige said, "Don't look back. Something might be gaining on you." It's a good way to summarize **repentance.** It means to turn away from sin. We disavow the old ways that displeased God, and damaged our lives.

Read Acts 26:20. What is the bottom line in demonstrating repentance?_____
_____*Actions — Deeds*_____

_____

_____

What are some "don't look back" issues from your old life? _____

_____

_____

_____

Leave the Driving to Us. You stop the car to pick up an important new client. But instead of climbing into the passenger seat, he comes around to the driver's side. "I'll drive," he says. Surprised, you reply that you'd be more comfortable doing the driving yourself (after all, you don't know him too well). He says, "I'm not getting into your car unless it's behind the wheel."

III. CHANGED BY ETERNAL LIFE

Surgery looms before you. As you sit in conference with the doctor, you have two concerns: What will the surgery be like? What will your life be like afterwards?

We have the same questions about our new birth in Christ. It is, after all, radical spiritual surgery. The Bible helps us understand what happens within us, and what changes.

Read 2 Corinthians 5:17. Describe the "surgery" that takes place within us.

All Things are New

Read Romans 8:9 and describe the "power shift" that takes place in believers.

We belong to Christ

IV. ASSURED OF ETERNAL LIFE

A father teaches his child to swim. Standing in the pool, he beckons for the little boy to jump from the side into his arms. The child sees the strong arms and trusts his dad — but it still takes courage to jump.

It's normal for Christians to have questions about their salvation. How can we know for sure about eternity? John, who knew Jesus, tells us the facts.

Read 1 John 5:11-13. In verses 11-12, what evidence of eternal life do we have? _He who has the son has life._

Testimony means a record or evidence.

According to John 10:25-30, who has the power to give eternal life, and where does eternal life come from? _____

What guarantee does Jesus give in verses 28, 29 of John 10?

What comes to your mind when the term "eternal life" is used? _____

_____

_____

_____

The Spirit Within. The Holy Spirit, God living in us, is an encourager. How does John 14:16,17 describe His ministry? _____

_____

What does Romans 8:16 add to this teaching? _____

_____

Changing Times. More evidence of eternal life: we begin to change! Why, according to 2 Corinthians 5:17, is this?

_____

_____

An Attitude Adjustment. One aspect of us that truly changes: our desire to please God. Read Paul's words in Philippians 3:7-8. How does he describe his change in attitude?

_____

_____

Later, in verses 12-14, Paul writes of his life in Christ. Describe his attitude. _____

> The Spirit of God comes to live within us when we accept Christ. He does many things: encouraging us, convicting us, teaching us, guiding us. He is our direct, everyday link to the things of eternity.

_____

_____

What motivates Paul to serve God? _____

_____

Love of Life. A final evidence that we've become something different is the love that grows within us. It's not love as the world defines it, but an unconditional, self-sacrificing love for our brothers and sisters. What does 1 John 3:14 say about love?

_____

_____

_____

Read 1 John 4:7-8. How does John account for this growth of love in us? _____

_____

Hooked on a feeling. What happens when we accept Christ into our lives? How does it feel? Are there fireworks? This is a natural question.

The answer simply depends on you. Have you ever signed a contract of huge significance, such as the mortgage on your first house? Have you ever signed a marriage license? These events shape your destiny in ways you can never fully comprehend at the time. They are also acts of the will, which may or may not include strong emotions. The contracts are no less binding.

Becoming a Christian is the acceptance of an invitation. God causes a profound change in our eternal destiny. We might laugh or cry or feel a quiet joy. The emotions are the icing, not the cake.

Don't worry: If you don't see fireworks, you're not missing the show!

V. ETERNAL LIFE NOW AND THEN

Pie in the Sky By and By? Sometimes we think of eternal life as a future reward for the trials of this life. Good news: The Bible teaches us the reward begins here and now! As a matter of fact, the Scripture always speak of eternal life in the present tense.

Read John 10:10. What kind of present life do you think Jesus describes?

_____

_____

_____

Read Galatians 2:20. What reason is given for the incredible life-change we experience?

_____

_____

According to John 14:6, what is Jesus' relationship to this life? _____

_____

_____

A Forever Family. Yet still, what we experience now is just a glimmer. We are promised that someday we will be in God's presence completely, that there will be no more suffering, and that we will be all He created us to be. It's simply more than our present minds can comprehend, and the Bible gives us only a few hints to nurture our hope.

How, in 1 Corinthians 13:12, does Paul contrast life now with life in heaven?

_____

_____

_____

_____

Read Philippians 3:20. What is our current relationship to heaven? _____

_____

_____

What "no-lose situation" does Paul describe in Philippians 1:21? Explain.

_____

_____

_____

Penalty, Power, and Presence.
To summarize the teachings from Romans, we are free from the penalty and power of sin, but not the presence of sin. Think again about surgery. The doctor has corrected the condition that caused your injury; the injury has no more power over you. But you must live in the same environment which caused the injury and often must live with the consequences (after effects) of that injury. You must care for your body and protect it from harm. We live in a world of sin, but we constantly remind ourselves it has no more power over us.

HERE TODAY, GOD'S TOMORROW.

It's the best kept secret around: Eternal life means "benefits" which begin right now. We face an eternity of joy, peace, and perfection; yet, because "to live is Christ," there is hope, fulfillment and abundant living available for this very moment. All in all, not a bad deal!

Summarize what you learned in this lesson about eternal life and its significance to you. _____

_____

_____

_____

_____

_____

_____

_____

_____

Scripture Memory Verse:

> **1 Assurance of Salvation**   NIV
>
> I JOHN 5:11-13
>   And this is the testimony: God has given us eternal life, and this life is in his Son. He who has the Son has life; he who does not have the Son of God does not have life. I write these things to you who believe in the name of the Son of God so that you may know that you have eternal life.
>
>   I JOHN 5:11-13

Why Memorize and Meditate on Scripture and How?

When Jesus was tempted by Satan in the wilderness (Matthew 4:1-11), three times Jesus replied: "It is written." Jesus then quoted particular and pertinent Scripture from the Old Testament to combat Satan's attack. In this passage we see that Satan quotes Scripture in a distorted way to tempt Jesus. Jesus used the appropriate Scripture to refute Satan and show his error. Matthew 4:11 states that Satan then left Christ.

If Christ found the Scriptures necessary to battle Satan, how much more do we need this weapon, the Word of God, for our lives. This week you will start hiding God's Word in your heart. Psalms 119:11 says "Thy Word have I hid in my heart that I might not sin against Thee [God]." God's Word strengthens and encourages us in the daily battles of life. In addition, it serves as a preventative to keep you from sinning against God. Key verses have been chosen to help you grow in your spiritual walk with the Lord. Work diligently to learn them. You are joining thousands of others who have found this the key to their spiritual growth.

Tear out the card in the back of this book on which I John 5:11-13 is printed. You may choose to memorize either the NIV (New International Version) or the KJV (King James Version). Read it several times, silently and aloud, to get an overall view of the content. Then, begin memorizing the verses, one phrase at a time. Each time you say the verse or a part of the verse, begin by repeating the reference, "I John 5:11-13." Also, say the reference after each time you repeat the verse or part of the verse. How many times have you heard or said, "There's a verse somewhere that says…"? Repeating the reference every time fixes its location in your memory.

God urges his people many times throughout Scripture to meditate on His Word and promises to bless them as a result. Once you have memorized the whole passage, begin to meditate on the verse. One way to do this is to repeat the verse, emphasizing a different word each time. Personalizing the verse often brings added insight and help: substitute personal pronouns into the verse, "me", "I", or your name. For instance, I John 5:11-13 personalized, would be:

"And this is the testimony: God has given me, _____ name _____ , eternal life, and this life is in his Son. If I have the Son I have life; if I do not have the Son of God I do not have life. These things were written to me, _____ name _____ , who believes in the name of the Son of God so that I may know that I have eternal life."

Caution: Make sure you know the verse word for word as it is written before you try to personalize or else you might get confused!

Review is the key to mastering and retaining these verses. So, every day, review I John 5:11-13. Next week, when you begin another verse, keep reviewing I John 5:11-13 daily while you are working on the new verse. The cards are small so they are conveniently portable in a purse or wallet, or they can be taped on your mirror for frequent review! As you encounter various situations and temptations during the week, you will be surprised to see how often God will bring these verses to mind to strengthen and sustain you.

NOTES

CHAPTER TWO
2 Discovering the Holy Spirit

That's What They Say:

The doctrine of the Holy Spirit is the Cinderella of Christian doctrines. Very few seem to be interested in it... Why, were it not for the work of the Holy Spirit there would be no gospel, no faith, no Church, no Christianity in the world at all.

J. I. PACKER, THEOLOGIAN

Jesus promised His followers that 'The Strengthener' would be with them forever. This promise is no lullaby for the faint-hearted. It is a blood transfusion for courageous living. E. PAUL HOVEY

The name of God carries an association for people across the globe, believers and non-believers alike. Most people know the name of Jesus, and have a mental image of the Man who walked the earth two thousand years ago.

Then there's the Holy Spirit. He's the neglected Person of the Trinity. Even His name is mysterious. For many believers, His work is equally obscure. Who is He? What does He mean to your life? The Bible has plenty to tell us about the Holy Spirit.

W A R M U P

What is the "Trinity?" Webster's defines it as "the unity of the Father, Son, and Holy Spirit as three persons in one godhead."

THE BIG PICTURE.

In this section we'll examine four questions:

I. Who is the Holy Spirit?
II. Who has the Holy Spirit?
III. What does the Holy Spirit do?
IV. How does one live and work with the Holy Spirit?

I. WHO IS THE HOLY SPIRIT?

The Holy Spirit is a Person — always described in Scripture as a "He," not an "It." He is one of the three Members of the Triune God. While we worship one Lord, He is expressed as Father, Son and Holy Spirit.

How old is the Holy Spirit? Read Genesis 1:2 and comment on the description of God's Spirit. ___WAs Her in the Beginning___

Because He is God, the Spirit has always been in existence. Read another passage from Old Testament times (before Jesus), Psalm 139:7-8. Where is the Spirit, according to these verses? ___The Spirit is every where___

The Self-Effacing Type. There's no doubt the Holy Spirit seems to keep a "lower profile" than the Father or the Son. Does this mean He is less important? How does Jesus describe the character of the Holy Spirit in John 16:13-14?

___He will not Speak on His own___

To fully comprehend the Trinity is beyond the capacity of our finite minds. But God has designed His creation to give us some pictures that help our understanding.

One Man
Three Functions

Father to his children

Son to his parents

Husband to his wife

One Egg
Three parts with
three distinct purposes

Shell – For protection ····················

White – For nourishment ····/

Yolk – For fertilization ····

Get the picture. The Holy Spirit never speaks of Himself. But what is He like? Let's look at some of the symbols used for Him in Scripture.

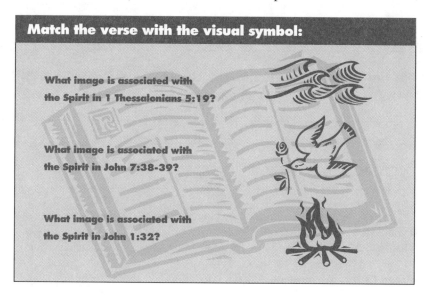

Match the verse with the visual symbol:

What image is associated with the Spirit in 1 Thessalonians 5:19?

What image is associated with the Spirit in John 7:38-39?

What image is associated with the Spirit in John 1:32?

He is as powerful as fire; as life-giving as water; as gentle as a dove; and brings the very anointing of God. We need to know more about this Spirit.

II. WHO HAS THE HOLY SPIRIT?

Good References. Read John 16:7. What does this verse tell us about Jesus' regard for the Holy Spirit ('Counselor')? _____

_____

In your opinion, what is the advantage of having the Holy Spirit instead of the physical presence of Jesus? _____

_____

_____

_____

Read John 7:38-39. For whom is the Spirit available? _____

_____

According to verse 39, why had the Spirit not been previously available? _____
_____
_____ *Jesus had not been Glorified* _____
_____

Our Special Guest. Read 1 Corinthians 3:16. Why is it important that God dwells
in us and we are described as His temple? _____
_____ *God's Spirit Lives in US.* _____
_____
_____
_____

What if you discovered the President of the United States was coming to visit your home?
Would you do a thorough cleaning? Would you worry about having everything at its
best? The Bible tells us that God Himself, in the Holy Spirit, is your permanent guest!

Members Only. We must also ask who does not have the Holy Spirit.

In John 14:17, why do people reject the Spirit? _____
_____ *They don't see him or Know him.* _____
_____

Read 1 Corinthians 2:14-16. Describe the difference between one who has the Spirit and
one who doesn't. _____
_____ *Foolish* _____
_____ *Cannot understand them* _____
_____

III. WHAT DOES THE HOLY SPIRIT DO?

Job Description. Now we know who the Holy Spirit is, and that He is available to all believers. Exactly what does He set out to accomplish?

Read John 14:26. What name is given to the Spirit? _____ Counselor _____

_____

What purpose is stated for the Spirit? _____ Teach & Remind _____

_____

How would you summarize the relationship between Jesus and the Spirit?

_____
Unified
_____

Read John 16: 7-15. What role of the Spirit is described in verses 8-11?

_____

_____

What role is mentioned in verse 13? _____

_____

What startling claim for the Spirit is made in verses 14-15? _____

_____

1 Corinthians 2:10-16 develops this idea further. What unique power is described in verses 10-11? _____

_____

According to verse 13, the Spirit also gives us the right _____

_____

What attribute does the Spirit bring us according to Acts 1:8? _____

_____

Gifts for Everyone. The Spirit is also the distributor of wonderful gifts. See the chart which lists some of them.

The gifts are often defined and grouped in various ways. Here is one way of looking at some of the gifts that the Holy Spirit gives to believers. If you have not identified your own spiritual gift(s), there are several excellent resources that provide a personal questionnaire to help you discern what they might be and how God might want to use your gifts to benefit the body of Christ and the world.

SPEAKING GIFTS

Prophecy	Speaks Biblical truth	EPHESIANS 4:11
		ROMANS 12:6
		I COR. 12:28
Teaching	Presents truth practically	EPHESIANS 4:11
		ROMANS 12:6
		I COR. 12:28

SERVICE GIFTS

Administration	Organizes well; productive	ROMANS 12:28
Helps	Desires to help meet needs	I COR. 12:28
Giving	Gives generously	ROMANS 12:8
Serving	Desires to help others	ROMANS 12:7

RELATIONAL GIFTS

Encouragement	Builds up; edifies others	ROMANS 12:7
Evangelism	Passion to share the gospel	EPHESIANS 4:18
Hospitality	Warm, inviting, giving nature	ROMANS 12:13
Leadership	Motivates others	ROMANS 12:8
Mercy	Sympathetic, tolerant	ROMANS 12:8
Shepherding	Caring and nurturing	EPHESIANS 4:11

Others that are sometimes included in this list are faith, healing, interpretation, knowledge, miracles, wisdom and apostleship.

IV. HOW DOES ONE LIVE AND WORK WITH THE HOLY SPIRIT?

Getting Your House in Order. A guest has come to stay in your home — indefinitely. This makes him a permanent part of your household, a part of the family! It means a reorganization of the home. It's the same way with the Holy Spirit. How are we to live with this new resident?

As we've seen, God now considers your body His temple. We might certainly behave differently in a place of worship than, say, a gymnasium. Read Romans 6:11-14. According to verse 11, what is the basic change we should consider?

_____

_____

What kind of offering should we make to God in the "temple"? (v.13)

_____

_____

Describe some of the good activities this passage might mean for your own life.

_____

_____

_____

_____

A Checkup from the Neck Up. Read Ephesians 4:23-32. List some of the new attitudes and approaches God intends for your life, according to this passage.

_____

_____

_____

What do you think it means to "grieve the Holy Spirit," based on verse 30?

_____

_____

The "seal" in verse 30 means a pledge — in modern business terms, a letter of intent. The Holy Spirit is God's mark on a person's life. What is your reaction to this idea?

_____

_____

Fresh Fruit in Season. Finally, we look for the evidence of the Holy Spirit's residence. He is a guest who truly beautifies His surroundings. Read Galatians 5:19-25. List the fruit. Does the list in verses 19-21 remind you of today's world? Explain.

_____

_____

_____

Why do you think Paul refers to the list in verses 22-23 as "fruit"?

_____

_____

What does he mean by the phrase "keep in step with the Spirit"? (v.25) _____

_____

_____

_____

What truth about the Holy Spirit from this study has most encouraged you? Explain your answer.

_____

_____

_____

_____

_____

_____

_____

Jesus' followers must have been shocked when He said they would be better off if He left. Yet we understand what He meant. The presence of the Holy Spirit means Christ lives within us. We have His mind, His guidance and power, wherever we go and for always. Yet despite this, we need each other all the more — the Spirit brings us together to be the Body of Christ and gives us gifts with which we build each other up. Indeed we continue learning to keep in step with the Spirit.

*Scripture
Memory
Verse:*

2 Fruit of the Holy Spirit   NIV

GALATIANS 5:22,23

But the fruit of the Spirit is love, joy, peace, patience, kindness, goodness, faithfulness, gentleness and self-control. Against such things there is no law.

GALATIANS 5:22,23

NOTES

> **REFLECTIONS**
>
> "It is not an accident of language that He is called the Holy Spirit, for whatever else the word holy may mean it does undoubtedly carry with it the idea of moral purity." A. Z. TOZER

3 Knowing Your Enemy

, GUYS, WE'VE READ THE OPPOSITION'S PLAYBOOK AND HE'S PRETTY PREDICTABLE, REALLY. LET'S REMEMBER OUR ASSIGNMENTS. AND ONE MORE THING: WATCH THE TRICK PLAY!

That's What They Say:

> *And Satan trembles when he sees, The weakest saint upon his knees.*
> WILLIAM COWPER (1731-1800)

> *There are two equal and opposite errors into which our race can fall about the devils. One is to disbelieve in their existence. The other is to believe, and to feel an excessive and unhealthy interest in them. They themselves are equally pleased by both errors.*
> C. S. LEWIS

WARM UP

The Devil has mastered the modern art of public relations.

Deny his existence? Our world is fascinated by him. He appears on the cover of rock albums, as a recurring character in TV situation comedies, and on the helmets of football teams. While his infernal image seems to be everywhere, it's really only an indication we don't take him or his power very seriously. And we do so at our own peril.

But there's a quick remedy for that: a survey of the Bible's description of Satan, the Father of Lies.

THE BIG PICTURE.

In this chapter we'll discuss four topics:

    I. Who is Satan?
    II. What is Satan's history and future?
    III. What is Satan's strategy?
    IV. What should be our strategy?

I. WHO IS SATAN?

A Little Name-Calling. Satan means "the adversary." But he has many other names and descriptions in Scripture. Let's see what we can learn about him through some of them.

Reference	How Satan is described
1 PETER 5:8	
1 THESSALONIANS 3:5	
MATTHEW 13:19	
JOHN 8:44	
JOHN 16:11	
2 CORINTHIANS 4:4	
2 CORINTHIANS 11:14	
1 JOHN 2:13	
REVELATION 12:9	
REVELATION 12:10	

In Genesis he is known as the serpent; in Revelation, the great dragon. He is alternately Satan, the devil, Belial, and Beelzebub, or Lucifer. One thing is certain: throughout the sixty-six books of our Bible, written over thousands of years, across continents, by many hands, the Evil One is always acknowledged, consistently depicted, and taken seriously.

II. WHAT IS SATAN'S HISTORY AND FUTURE?

From Top to Bottom. Since the Bible covers the entire span of history, we know a bit about Satan's origin, as well as something about his ultimate fate. Would you be surprised to learn that God created him? That he was once an angel? Two passages, from Isaiah and Ezekiel, seem to be referring to his history.

Read Ezekiel 28:11-19. List some facts about the "guardian cherub" as he was created.

_____

_____

Read Isaiah 14:12-15. Some translations use the term "Lucifer" or "day-star" as synonyms for Satan. Evidently, Satan has a strong will. What do we learn from his five "I will's" in this Scripture? _____

_____

An old saying: "Pride goes before a fall." In both these passages, what ultimately happens to the devil?_____

_____

What glimpse of Satan's future is given in Matthew 25:41?

_____

_____

_____

_____

1 John 3:8 says Jesus came to _____

_____

_____

What is the final destiny of Satan, described in Revelation 20:1-3, 10?_____

_____

_____

_____

_____

Devil of a Time. The "Prince of This World" has his day in the sun. He causes human pain and wages war against the Creator who cast him out. But God has written the last word, and already announced his fate. Jesus neutralized Satan's ultimate weapon — death — two thousand years ago, and Christians need not fear the devil. Satan does nothing without God's knowledge. God has ultimate control.

III. WHAT IS SATAN'S STRATEGY?

Smooth Operator. We've learned much about Satan from his Biblical names and descriptions. We can learn even more from observing him in action. Let's observe two particular case studies.

Case Study A: Adam and Eve

Read Genesis 3:1-5. You might recall that the first man and woman were given one command: not to eat of one particular tree.

In verse 1, what question does Satan pose to Eve? _____

_____

Eve repeated God's words, adding her own twist that God said not to even touch it. In verses 4-5, how does the serpent respond? _____

_____

Case Study B: Jesus

Jesus is sometimes called "the Second Adam" (see Romans 5). He, too, faced Satan's deception. Read Matthew 4:1-11.

How does Satan first tempt Jesus? (v.3) _____

_____

In verses 5-6, what does the devil use to entice?_____

_____

_____

In verses 8-9, what are the stakes? _____

_____

_____

What personal goal does Satan reveal? _____

_____

_____

In all cases, how does Jesus counter temptation? _____

_____

_____

In these two studies, what parallels can you find in the devil's strategy?

_____

_____

_____

_____

In Luke 22:31, how is Satan's work described? _____

_____

_____

Now we know something about how Satan works. Forewarned is fore-armed! But we need a cohesive battle plan. In the next section, we'll put one together.

IV. WHAT SHOULD BE OUR STRATEGY?

The Best Offense is a Good Defense. The great football teams excel "on both sides of the ball;" that is, their offensive and defensive teams come prepared with an effective game plan. But the most respected coaches will tell you that games are most often won by the defense.

Read Ephesians 6:11-18. What adversaries are described in verse 12?

_____

_____

List the elements of "spiritual armor" laid out for us in verses 13-17.

_____

_____

_____

_____

_____

Explain the importance of the kind of prayer described in verse 18.

_____

_____

_____

Ephesians 4:27 mentions another defensive formation. What do you think Paul is referring to? _____

_____

_____

_____

How is Satan described in 1 Peter 5:8-9? _____

_____

What is helpful about the knowledge described in verse 9? _____

_____

_____

_____

What is the "bottom line," according to John 16:11? _____

_____

_____

_____

Getting Offensive. Finally, there are some things Christians can do to "take the battle to" the Evil One.

Read Revelation 12:11. What are the weapons which overcome Satan?

_____

_____

James 4:7 tells us to submit ourselves to God. What is the indicator of this, according to 1 John 2:3-4? _____

_____

_____

How can obedience to God's commandments thwart the devil's work?

_____

_____

The Scouting Report. Reflect on the week (or "weak"?) ahead. Where are your pressure points? Decide on some times and places you would expect Satan to look for a foothold. What offensive and defensive strategies will form an effective game plan for you?

SCOUTING REPORT

OFFENSIVE STRATEGIES:

_____

_____

_____

_____

DEFENSIVE STRATEGIES:

_____

_____

_____

_____

The Final Score. An enthusiastic football fan videotapes the games of his favorite team. He sweats through the actual contests, but he enjoys the tape. "It's amazing how much stress is removed when you know how it all comes out," he smiles.

The Bible records all the "game highlights" of our history — past, present and future. The winner has already been decided. For those of us who are believers, the game must still be played every day. But we can view it with excitement and confidence when we know the final score. God wins — and so do we.

Scripture Memory Verse:

3 The Adversary   NIV

I PETER 5:8,9
Be self-controlled and alert. Your enemy the devil prowls around like a roaring lion looking for someone to devour. Resist him, standing firm in the faith, because you know that your brothers throughout the world are undergoing the same kind of sufferings.

I PETER 5:8,9

NOTES

_____

_____

_____

_____

_____

_____

_____

_____

_____

_____

_____

_____

_____

_____

4 Dealing with Temptation

I EAT ONE OF THESE THINGS EVERY DAY, THEN FEEL GUILTY, GO HOME AND TELL MY WIFE, THEN I FEEL BETTER. YET I KEEP GAINING WEIGHT! ANY SUGGESTIONS?

That's What They Say...

A little girl, asked about temptation, said, "Well, when I hear Satan come knocking at the door of my heart, I just ask Jesus to go to the door. And when He opens the door, Satan draws away and says, 'Oh! Excuse me, I have made a mistake.'"
DONALD GREY BARNHOUSE

Obedience is the key to all doors; feelings come (or don't come) and go as God pleases. We can't produce them at will, and mustn't try. C. S. LEWIS

WARM UP

Lost and Found. The flight was pleasant, the rental car is fun to drive, and your city map has kept you on course — until now. Suddenly, you are not finding the landmarks you expected. The street names aren't found on your (apparently dated) map. Fortunately, you had jotted down the phone number of your host, just in case.

When we travel the path of a believer, we also encounter unexpected twists and turns. The Christian way includes no "cruise control" feature. Fortunately, we're given a road map which does not go out of date, and we can call on our heavenly Host at any time.

THE BIG PICTURE.

In this chapter, we'll discuss "travel tips" pertaining to obedience, temptation, and confession. We'll examine four areas:

    I. What happens when I fail?
    II. How can I find the path again?
    III. How do I obey God and stay on the path?
    IV. The fruits of obedience

I. WHAT HAPPENS WHEN I FAIL?

On the Road Again. Back to that business trip to a strange city. You find yourself lost, and you're the type who hates to stop and ask for directions. Your spouse would have a good laugh at your dilemma. You have several choices: ask for help immediately; get a better map; or "tough it out" by wandering until you find your way.

Sadly, many choose that third option when it comes to life's big questions. They wander through life without a clue about which way to go. In this section, we'll deal with the question of temptation.

Your Heart's Desire. Read James 1:13-15. What is the source of temptation?

_____

_____

How can temptation cause us to be "dragged away" from the right path, according to these verses? _____

_____

_____

What three assurances about temptation are given in 1 Corinthians 10:13?

_____

_____

_____

_____

The Voice of Experience. Read Hebrews 4:14-16. What part does Jesus play in our temptations? _____

_____

_____

How, in your opinion, might it help you to know this? _____

_____

_____

_____

What should you do when you face temptation, according to verse 16?

_____

_____

_____

_____

_____

_____

_____

_____

_____

_____

BEEN THERE, DONE THAT.

Jesus is one to Whom we can never say, "You wouldn't understand." He's been there. And He always knows the way out. We face temptation every day, and He will always provide the strength we need to overcome it. But we don't always overcome or obey. The failure that results is called sin, and in the next section we'll explore what to do next.

II. HOW DO I FIND THE PATH AGAIN?

True Confessions. One of life's toughest assignments is admitting when we're wrong — or that we're lost. At some point we have to get back on the right road. For Christians, there's a necessary step known as confession. Let's find out what Scripture says about it.

What two purposes for confession are given in 1 John 1:9? _____

_____

_____

_____

In the next chapter of I John (2:12) we see that actually, our sins are already forgiven. Why, then, is it important that we confess our sins?

_____

_____

_____

_____

Confessing Christians. There is another kind of confession other than what we tell God privately. Read James 5:16. What two activities are described?

_____

_____

Do you have access to the kind of Christian friend described here? Write the name(s) of a person or persons with whom you can share deep needs and pray.

_____

_____

_____

_____

III. HOW DO I OBEY GOD AND STAY ON THE PATH?

It's one thing to speak of obeying one's parents, or one's supervisor, or the authorities. We can see and hear them. But how, exactly, do we obey God? How can we know we're on the "straight and narrow path?"

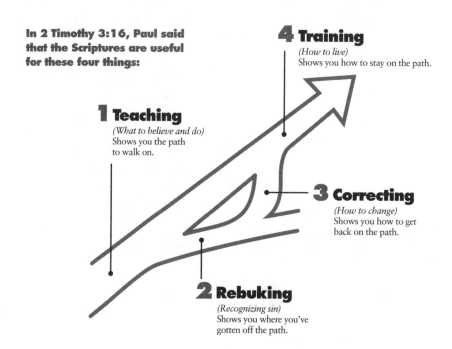

In 2 Timothy 3:16, Paul said that the Scriptures are useful for these four things:

4 Training
(How to live)
Shows you how to stay on the path.

1 Teaching
(What to believe and do)
Shows you the path to walk on.

3 Correcting
(How to change)
Shows you how to get back on the path.

2 Rebuking
(Recognizing sin)
Shows you where you've gotten off the path.

Read John 10:27. What does Jesus say His followers will do? _____

_____

_____

_____

What important element of discerning God's will is affirmed in 2 Timothy 3:16?

_____

_____

What does Psalm 119:11 point out that we can do? _____

_____

How, in your opinion, will memorization of Scripture encourage us to be obedient?

_____

_____

_____

1 John 2:6 adds another way we can be obedient. What is it?

_____

_____

Charles Sheldon's classic novel, *In His Steps,* tells the fictional story of a group of people who took 1 John 2:6 seriously: They decided to ask themselves, in all their decisions, what Jesus would do and then do it. Needless to say, incredible things began to happen!

Obedience is a matter of body, soul, mind, and spirit. How does Romans 6:12-14 say we can be obedient with our bodies? _____

_____

_____

_____

What areas of your life do you feel this passage applies to? _____

_____

_____

_____

_____

Matthew 7:7 gives a simple approach for finding God's will. In your own words, explain Jesus' teaching in this verse. _____

_____

_____

_____

Another important element of obedience is found in Proverbs 13:20. Why do you think this instruction is important? _____

_____

Jesus says His sheep will hear His voice, and follow. We hear Him in Scripture, and through prayer. We follow the example of Jesus Himself. We seek the counsel of wise Christians. He will always be there to provide clear guidance. The question is generally not one of understanding, but of will. In the next section we explore what happens when we stray from the path.

IV. THE FRUITS OF OBEDIENCE

If only obedience came naturally! Anyone who has ever been a parent (or a child) knows that it doesn't. Children are born with an inclination to rebel, and it has been this way since Adam and Eve failed their first test. Kids come to a point at which they must ask, "why obey my parents?" Similarly, Christians face the same question with the Lord.

What simple motivation for obedience is given in John 14:21? _____

_____

How does love result in obedience? _____

_____

_____

_____

Read again John 14:21. What further developments spring from loving obedience? ___

_____

_____

_____

Psalm 119:9 tells us that obeying God will help us keep _____

_____

Matthew 7:24-27 offers a parable of Jesus. Summarize the message of this story in your own words. _____

_____

_____

_____

Follow the Leader. We obey God as a grateful response to His love; because it leads to knowing Him more intimately; and because it brings a life of purity and excellence. Let's also add that obedience to God is the only *sane* way to live in a world He created. Every other path leads to self-destruction. As you travel, always keep in mind Paul's words:

ROMANS 12:11-12 "Never be lacking in zeal, but keep your spiritual fervor, serving the Lord. Be joyful in hope, patient in affliction, faithful in prayer."

God our Father.
Read Hebrews 12:1-13. What is encouraging to you in this passage?

_____

_____

_____

What is difficult for you in this passage?

_____

_____

_____

Reflect back on this study. What new insight(s) did God reveal to you?

_____

_____

_____

_____

_____

_____

_____

_____

_____

Scripture Memory Verse:

4 Assurance of Deliverance   NIV

I CORINTHIANS 10:13

No temptation has seized you except what is common to man. And God is faithful; he will not let you be tempted beyond what you can bear. But when you are tempted, he will also provide a way out so that you can stand up under it.

I CORINTHIANS 10:13

NOTES

5 Your Calling as an Insider

"*Where to serve is among the first issues in our call to discipleship. We are to serve Christ as insiders in an unbelieving world. Many of us have withdrawn from our old associations to where we have all but lost our insidership. In a sense we have abandoned a post that was uniquely ours, that cannot be filled by another in exactly the same way.*   JIM PETERSEN, LIFESTYLE DISCIPLESHIP

During the reign of Oliver Cromwell, the British government began to run low on silver for coins. Lord Cromwell sent his men on an investigation of the local cathedral to see if they could find any precious metal there…. They reported: 'The only silver we could find is the statues of the saints standing in the corners.' To which the radical soldier and statesman of England replied: 'Good! We'll melt down the saints and put them into circulation!'… Sunday go-to-meetin' silver saints in shining armor are simply out of circulation if that's the limit to their faith.   CHARLES SWINDOLL, COME BEFORE WINTER"

WARM UP

If you want your book to be a best-seller, here's a tip: Imprint on its cover the subtitle "An Insider Tells All." No one can resist hearing inside information. We want to know how movie stars live; how millionaires made their fortune; what it's like in the major league clubhouse.

Christians often have the mistaken impression that becoming an insider in the kingdom of God means becoming an outsider to the world. On the contrary, we're called "in" instead of "out."

"An Insider Tells All"

THE BIG PICTURE.

In this section, we'll discuss four aspects of our calling as insiders:

I. **What is an insider?**
II. **How can I be an insider?**
III. **How can I survive as an insider?**
IV. **What is an insider's vision?**

> The term "insider" means one who lives "in" the world, but is not "of" the world. He recognizes that where he lives and works is God's unique and primary mission field for him.

I. WHAT IS AN INSIDER?

Inside Out. In his book, *Lifestyle Discipleship* (Colorado Springs: Navpress, 1993) Jim Petersen makes the case that "our basic strategy for connecting with an unbelieving world is going to have to change." In the past, we've assumed that if we opened the church doors, sooner or later the world would come to us. If it were ever true, it's no longer so. We are here for the sake of the lost, not just to change society.

IN THE TRENCHES.

Jesus, though divine, identified with the lowly; Paul, a proud Pharisee and Roman citizen, was "all things to all men." They changed the world from the inside out.

There are times, of course, when God calls us out. After a number of years, Paul was called to leave his life as a Pharisee "insider" because God needed him elsewhere in the world. Even then, he was vigorously involved with non-believers everywhere he went.

We begin with our foundation: Jesus, the ultimate insider. Read Philippians 2:5-8. How does this description establish Jesus as an insider? _____

_____

Verse 5 says we should match the attitude. What do you think this means? _____

_____

From whatever facts you know about Jesus, how did He function as an insider in His world? _____

_____

Paul describes his "insidership" in 1 Corinthians 9:19-23. What goal does he describe? (vv.19, 22) _____

_____

Summarize his strategy as detailed in the passage. _____

_____

_____

_____

The Living Proof I Evangelism Video Series, Session 4 describes this as "common ground."

The Principle of Common Ground

I Corinthians 9:19-23

Looking for areas of common ground.

In thinking of building a friendship with a non-Christian, check the activities below that might be appropriate areas of common ground.

- ☐ Tennis
- ☐ Sewing
- ☐ Camping
- ☐ Music concerts
- ☐ Hunting
- ☐ Theater
- ☐ Swimming
- ☐ Gambling
- ☐ Picnics

- ☐ P.T.A.
- ☐ Rotary club
- ☐ Garden club
- ☐ Sunday school
- ☐ Dinner out
- ☐ Playing bridge
- ☐ Questionable movies
- ☐ Going to sports events
- ☐ Shady business deals

- ☐ Wednesday night prayer meetings
- ☐ Swapping dirty jokes
- ☐ Entertaining at home
- ☐ Boating
- ☐ Attending a social function where alcohol is served

II. How Can I Be An Insider?

Easier said than done! Wait; doesn't 1 John 2:15 tell us not to love the world, and aren't we told that light has no fellowship with darkness? If Christ truly changes us, how can we possibly be insiders in the world?

Read 1 Corinthians 7:17, 20, and 26. What command is repeated three times?

_____

_____

Paul tells us that when God reaches us, He usually has us right where He wants us. Unless our work or status itself is specifically unpleasing to God (for example, criminal acts, or, in Paul's case, his persecution of believers), we should hold our position and use it for Him.

How should our behavior be characterized, according to 1 Peter 2:12?

_____

_____

What word does Paul use to describe our lives in 1 Thessalonians 4:7?

_____

_____

What two word pictures does Jesus use in Matthew 5:13-16 to describe our relationship to the world? Explain each. _____

_____

_____

_____

Taking the field. It has been said that if our world is a great football stadium, too many Christians are watching from the stands. The action is inside the gridiron. Many of us are emotional spectators, cheering for God's cause and getting upset when the team does poorly on the field. God calls us out of the cheap seats and into the action — until the game is won.

One warning, however: if you're going onto the field, you'd better be ready for battle!

III. HOW CAN I SURVIVE AS AN INSIDER?

The weary traveller. Ever travelled abroad? The best part was returning home, wasn't it? In another country, we discover the perils of different languages and unfamiliar customs. It can be a lonely feeling.

In spiritual terms, the Christian lives such a life. We'd love to rest and prop up our feet in heaven — or at least with the church crowd — all the time. Instead, we're full time travellers in a foreign world, citizens of heaven (see Philippians 3:20). Don't leave without your travel kit!

Read John 17:20-23. What is Jesus' prayer for his disciples, expressed in verse 21?

_____

_____

How might this help us survive in the world as insiders? _____

_____

_____

_____

According to verse 23, in what way are we identified with the Father and the Son?

_____

_____

The first believers had a dramatic impact on their world as insiders. Read Acts 2:46-47 and describe their fellowship. _____

_____

What was the result? (v.47) _____

_____

Strength in numbers. True Christian community, then, strengthens and sustains us as we live in the world — as does the reality of Christ within us.

MARGIN

There is another essential consideration for surviving as a Christian insider. Richard Swensen, M.D. calls it *margin* in his book of that name (Colorado Springs: Navpress, 1992).* He defines margin as "the leeway we once had between ourselves and our limits," the uncluttered space in our lives available as a reserve. Many of us today are working at capacity — physically, spiritually, mentally, and emotionally. This monopoly on our energies robs us of time and the freedom we need to be effective as Christian insiders (not to mention as family members, employees, friends, or anything else). To keep our edge in the modern world, margin must be maintained.

Dr. Swensen gives a mathematical definition of margin: Power – Load = Margin. "When our load is greater than our power, we enter into negative margin status, that is, we are overloaded." (p. 92)

Keeping margin in our lives is critical if we're going to have vision, our final consideration in this chapter.

How might remaining as an insider in your work or in your neighborhood give you margin? _____

_____

_____

*A practical study on "Margin" can be ordered through CBMC headquarters.

IV. WHAT IS AN INSIDER'S VISION?

Hang in there! Think of a time when you worked long and hard, and it was all you could do to persevere. What got you through? Probably vision. You had a goal to reach, something to bank your hopes on — the kind of faith Hebrews 11:1 calls "the assurance of things hoped for, the conviction of things not seen." As an insider living in the world, you'll need such a vision.

Just before ascending to heaven, Jesus makes His vision statement in Matthew 28:19-20. What is His vision for His followers? _____

_____

What is Paul's vision in Col. 1:28,29? _____

_____

We see, then, that our vision is reaching the world. How do we achieve that end?

_____

In John 15:5, Jesus talks about fruit-bearing. What is the key to fruit-bearing?

_____

_____

Smooth sailing.

There's no doubt about it: Christians are called to navigate some turbulent waters. Just as any good ship needs a compass, we must keep our bearings at all times. We do so by maintaining His vision for us and for the world.

We must hold our ground in the world as spiritual soldiers. We have to stay involved as insiders if we're ever to make a difference. To do that, we must have unity in Christian fellowship, maintaining margin in our lives so Christ's vision, known as the Great Commission, will stay ever before us.

Above all else, if we allow Christ to live in and through us, God will use us as He accomplishes His purposes for this world.

> "Busyness rapes relationships. It substitutes shallow frenzy for deep friendship. It promises satisfying dreams, but delivers hollow nightmares. It feeds the ego, but starves the inner man. It fills the calendar but fractures the family. It cultivates a program, but plows under priorities."
>
> CHARLES SWINDOLL
> KILLING GIANTS, PULLING THORNS

Take An Insider Inventory

Take a walk on the *In*-side. By evaluating the various settings and people in your life, you can determine those places in which you're an established insider. Consider it your little plot of land in which God has placed you to till the soil. Who are some people in the categories below — and others you might think of — for whom God might want you to be salt and light?

At Home:

_____

_____

_____

At Work:

_____

_____

**In the
Neighborhood:**

_____

_____

_____

**I AM
AN INSIDER**

With Other People:

_____

_____

_____

At Other Places:

_____

_____

**With my Friends
and Social Circle:**

_____

_____

_____

Marginal Success

What if you were given the next three years to live? And what if you were told you not only had to accomplish your life's work in those three years — but you had to change human history? Would you carry an observable sense of urgency? Keep a hectic pace?

Consider that Jesus lived under these conditions. He understood and accepted His destiny, and made it clear to His followers. But here's the strange part: He never hurried anywhere. He always had time for people in His path. He found time to pray and be alone. He was calmer and more in control than you or me. His secret was that He understood His priorities.

In the space below, evaluate the margin in various areas of your life — that is, how close to empty are you operating? Understanding your responsibilities and limitations, how much margin is left to serve God in these areas? Use the fuel gauge to determine whether you have a "full tank," or you're "running on empty," or where you are in-between. When you have margin, you have reserves to call upon. When you are overloaded, your tank is "empty," and you have no more to give. Write any comments or insights you have about each area and how you might reduce your "overload" in these areas.

My Family Life
E   F
_____
_____
_____

My Friendships
E   F
_____
_____
_____

My Church Life
E   F
_____
_____
_____

My Work
E   F
_____
_____
_____

My Recreation
E   F
_____
_____
_____

My Finances
E   F
_____
_____
_____

Scripture Memory Verse:

5 Your Calling as an Insider   NIV

I CORINTHIANS 7:24
Brothers, each man, as responsible to God, should remain in the situation God called him to.

I CORINTHIANS 7:24

NOTES

"Just when you thought you were winning the rat race along come faster rats."

BUMPER STICKER

Telling Others About Christ

GEE, I OUGHTA TELL ED ABOUT THIS—EXCEPT I REALLY DON'T HAVE ENOUGH DETAILS. I'M NO EXPERT ON PARACHUTES. HE MIGHT NOT BELIEVE IT, ANYWAY, AND I WOULD FEEL FOOLISH...

DEFECTIVE PARACHUTES RECALLED

That's What They Say:

In order to live, we have to breathe both in and out. Evangelism is needed as the outgo in the Christian faith. DAVID READ

How can Christians be the salt of the earth if they never get out of the salt shaker?
REBECCA MANLEY PIPPERT

WARM UP

Spread the word! Your alma mater just won the NCAA basketball championship. Your daughter has been named valedictorian of her class. You and your spouse are sweepstakes winners of an all-expense-paid cruise to the Bahamas. You've received a large promotion and raise.

A pretty good week? You're thinking about shouting it from your rooftop, maybe taking an ad out in the paper to fill everyone in. Good news is made for sharing.

What if something happened to you that was better than all of the above — combined? That's the situation Christians find themselves in.

THE BIG PICTURE.

In this lesson, we'll discuss the art of sharing wonderful news. We'll discuss four categories:

> **I. Why should I tell others?**
> **II. What should I say?**
> **III. Who should I tell?**
> **IV. What is my testimony?**

I. WHY SHOULD I TELL OTHERS?

No Ask, No Tell. Have you ever heard any of these? "Religion is a private matter." "No one should force their interpretation on others." "Believe what you want, but leave me out of it."

Suggest a few reasons why Christians might be hesitant to share their faith.

_____

_____

What essential motivation is found in Acts 4:12? _____

_____

What is the subject of Jesus' "farewell address" in Matthew 28:19-20?

_____

What three instructions are given?_____

_____

_____

What are the implications of Mark 8:38 for us? _____

_____

In Philemon, verse 6, what is a positive motivator for sharing our faith? _____

_____

Can't Stop Talking. We share our faith because it is a command. It was Jesus' ultimate teaching for us before His ascension. But we do so also out of love, because "salvation is found in no one else,"(Acts 4:12) and because we want our friends to have the abundant life we have found. But how do we begin?

II. WHAT SHOULD I SAY?

Finding the Words. Oh, you'd love to present the gospel; you just need to get around to getting that seminary degree first, right? Actually, the Bible teaches that all Christians can share their faith. It doesn't take a rocket scientist. Let's look at the message.

Read 1 Peter 3:15,16. What is Peter's approach to evangelism? _____

_____

Why are we to have this kind of attitude? _____

_____

Like a good scout, then, we should "be prepared." Yet some of the preparation is already taken care of, according to Acts 1:8. Study that verse and explain the statement.

_____

_____

The Bottom Line. The basic message is contained in one simple verse, John 3:16 — sometimes called "the gospel in a nutshell." Use your own words to rephrase and explain that verse.

_____

_____

Paul presented the gospel everywhere he went. 1 Corinthians 15:1-6 illustrates his simple explanation of it. Outline his main points. _____

_____

_____

THAT'S HIS STORY AND I'M STICKING TO IT.

The basic gospel message never changes. God loves us; we fail to live up to His standards; He became a man and claimed our penalty so we could be brought home to Him. But there's another element to your presentation: just as you share His story, you must also share your own. It's called your testimony.

III. WHO SHOULD I TELL?

So Many People, So Little Time. How many people do you encounter in a day? At work; in restaurants; on planes; at the store: You probably come into contact with more than you think. Just when, where, how, and with whom can you share the gospel?

There is a way to witness twenty-four hours a day! What is it, according to Matthew 5:16?

_____

_____

What does it mean to "let your light shine?" Give the answer from 1 Peter 2:12.

_____

_____

Three levels of sharing our faith:
1. Raising the Flag
2. Faith Stories
3. Testimony

It's important to be sensitive to the moment in sharing Christ with an unbeliever. The Holy Spirit will prod you at the right time, and give you the words. But what you say, and how much you share, is affected by such factors as how well and how long you've known your friend, and what your surroundings are at the time. There are times when a hard-hitting, involved testimony can be self-defeating. We will briefly describe raising the flag and faith stories, and we will concentrate on preparing our testimony.

1. Raising the Flag: A flag clearly communicates the allegiance of the one raising it. In casual conversation, it can be easy — and non-threatening — to raise the flag of your faith by mentioning that a prayer has been answered, or that God has been dealing with you recently on an issue. It's also easy to make a reference to a good illustration from the pastor's sermon. These gentle "flags" establish your status as a Christian.

Raising the Flag Principles:
† It should happen as a natural part of a conversation
† If it takes more than thirty seconds, you're probably saying too much.
† Its purpose is to establish your identity as a member of God's family, not as a member of a religious denomination or affiliation.

2. Faith Stories: A faith story is a more direct way to talk about the presence of God in your life. While less than a full testimony, it's instead an anecdote about God's love and grace in one specific instance in your life — how He got you through a difficult time, how His blessing came at just the right time. A good, polished faith story will always command attention and open doors.

Faith Story Principles:
† A short story of when a Biblical truth made an impact on your life
† Its purpose is to create hunger in the unbeliever

Examples:
† Learning something new about business from the Bible
† Making a decision about work, family or relationships based on the Bible

3. Testimony: Paul had many months in prison to prepare his testimony before King Agrippa (Acts 26). The result was a sharp, brief life testimony no one could deny or attack. In Operation Timothy, you'll spend some time polishing the story of your conversion. It's one of your most precious tools as a Christian.

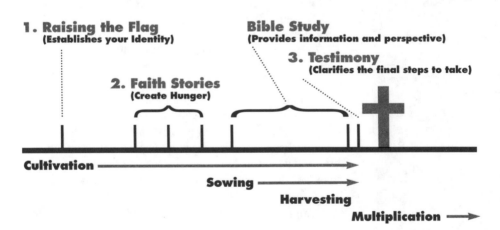

1. Raising the Flag
(Establishes your Identity)

Bible Study
(Provides information and perspective)

3. Testimony
(Clarifies the final steps to take)

2. Faith Stories
(Create Hunger)

Cultivation ————————————————→

Sowing ————————→

Harvesting ————————→

Multiplication ——→

Review Living Proof I, Evangelism Video Series, Sessions 2-8, which illustrate these principles through an unfolding drama about several people's lives and how they deal with these issues. If you have never seen this series, you can receive in-depth training in sharing your faith by participating in a Living Proof group that goes through all twelve sessions.

IV. WHAT IS MY TESTIMONY?

Putting Your Story to Work.

"I wish I could turn this conversation around and tell him about Christ."

"If there were only more time, I could tell him what Christ means to me."

"I wish I could remember those verses about how someone can receive Christ."

"If Paul were here, he could really explain how to become a Christian."

How often have these thoughts crossed your mind as opportunities to share Christ? You can turn day-to-day situations into exciting opportunities to share your faith by preparing ahead of time. Peter admonished us in I Peter 3:15 to be ready.

 I PETER 3:15 "But in your hearts set apart Christ as Lord. Always be prepared to give an answer to everyone who asks you to give the reason for the hope that you have."

> "The skeptic may deny your doctrine or attack your church but he cannot honestly ignore the fact that your life has been changed. He may stop his ears to the presentations of a preacher and the pleadings of an evangelist, but he is somehow attracted to the human-interest story of how you — John Q. Public — found peace within.
>
> CHARLES R. SWINDOLL,
> COME BEFORE WINTER

Any subject can be presented more effectively by careful organization. A carefully prepared testimony, given in the power of the Holy Spirit, can be of immediate and effective use in nearly every witnessing situation. It should be our desire to present Christ in such a clear and attractive, yet simple, way that those who hear will not only want to know Him, but they will want to know Him in a personal way.

A carefully worded, concise testimony will communicate far more effectively than a prolonged presentation that includes a lot of extraneous material. The key is to minimize details that detract from, rather than emphasize, the point of personal commitment to Christ and what this can mean in a person's life. What are the essentials for effectively presenting the gospel? Fortunately, God has left us a model to follow. In Acts 26 we find Paul before King Agrippa giving his testimony. Read Acts 26 before going on. Here are a few ways that you might personalize these same principles in your own testimony.

1. GRACIOUS INTRODUCTION

ACTS 26:2,3   "…I consider myself fortunate to stand before you today as
I make my defense…"

Describe Paul's etiquette in verses 2 and 3. _____

_____

_____

Notice that Paul referred to Agrippa's knowledge of Jewish customs. Find a point of
common interest or identification. You might say to a friend, "You and I have a lot
in common, Pete. When I was in school, I had everything a fellow could want, but
underneath there was a lot of dissatisfaction." If the person has children, something
along the following lines might be appropriate: "Bringing up children in this modern
world is nearly impossible. Apart from one factor, I'd be utterly lost as to what to do."
You should have several possible introductions you could use in a variety of situations.

2. GOOD PART OF PAST LIFE

ACTS 26:4,5   "…I lived as a Pharisee…"

What is Paul's strategy in these verses? _____

_____

_____

If you just say what a sinner you were, people won't identify themselves with you.
Paul told how he was looked up to for his religious practices. If relevant, mention
briefly your good points from a worldly sense, like morality, church attendance, ideas
about God, generosity, as you lead to the third point.

3. BAD PART OF PAST LIFE

ACTS 26:9-11 — "…I, too, was convinced that I ought to do all that was possible to
oppose the name of Jesus…"

How does Paul attempt to intrigue his listeners in verses 9-11?

_____

_____

_____

"Even though people thought that I was so good, I knew what went on inside." Mention some specific things such as hateful thoughts, covetousness, emptiness of heart, or pride. Perhaps you feared that you would not go to heaven. Many will identify with you in this — they're not sure they're going to heaven either.

4. CIRCUMSTANCES OF CONVERSION

ACTS 26:12-15 "Who are you, Lord?"

What were some of the details that Paul included in his story?

_____

_____

_____

_____

> Christ's story,
> His death for our sins
> and His resurrection
> should be central
> in your story.

Don't feel your own story is colorless compared to Paul's. Your conversion is as much a miracle as his. Your testimony doesn't have to be exciting, just interesting and "real" to your audience. Use details which show the personal transaction with God, and avoid confusing statements like "I went forward at church," lest your listener thinks going forward is the answer. Instead, use, "When the minister asked if I had received Christ personally, I knew that I had not and that this was the time I must trust Him." If you do not know the exact time you were saved, you could say: "The time came when I realized what I was doing was not enough, but that Jesus' death on the cross provided my salvation." We know the sun rises at an exact moment, but we may not have seen it right then. Yet we know it is there because we see it in the sky.

5. RESULTS OF CONVERSION

ACTS 26:16-22 "I was not disobedient to the vision from heaven."

What were some of the results of Paul's encounter with Jesus?

_____

_____

_____

_____

Mention the most striking change in your life, as Paul did — whether in desires, actions, hunger for God's Word, peace, or satisfaction. Show the effects of your being born-again. Be realistic. Don't imply that Christ eliminates all the problems of life, but rather that He enables you to live them out with peace and confidence.

6. GOSPEL MESSAGE

ACTS 26:23 "that the Christ would suffer and, as the first to rise from the dead..."

Why is it important that Paul included this in his story?

_____

_____

_____

Christ's story, His death for our sins and His resurrection, must be interwoven into your story. Without His resurrection you would not have a story worth telling. Emphasize that the difference in your life was accepting Jesus Christ as Lord and Savior.

The order of Paul's story reflects the situation he was in and the people he was speaking to. Your message must have this type of flexibility. For example, you may find it beneficial to include the gospel explanation in point 4, making it part of the explanation of how you came to Christ. This portion of your testimony should include verses of Scripture.

7. PERSONAL APPEAL

ACTS 26:24-29 "That...you may become what I am..."

How does Paul make his case to Festus in verses 24-27?

_____

_____

_____

Using the listener's name, ask a question relating to him. "Bob, have you ever thought of Christ in this personal way?" Or, "Does what I have said bring any questions to your mind?"

Now, you're ready to prepare your story.

Use the three-point outline on the next page (before, how, after) to quickly list the major points as they come to mind. When you write it out in more detail, keep it between 700 and 1000 words (if typewritten, about four double-spaced pages). This will allow you to stay within three to five minutes when you give it verbally. Many have found it helpful to take a first-pass at their testimony verbally and have a friend identify and jot down the major points on the outline.

As you begin, ask God to give you the right words and approach. Trust Him to do it. This is as much His story as it is yours.

Personal Testimony Sheet

1. BEFORE:

1. What were some of your personal goals in life before you became a Christian?

_____

_____

2. What were some of the things that caused you to begin considering a personal relationship with Jesus Christ for yourself? (good part of past life; bad part of past life)

_____

_____

_____

_____

3. Before you made the decision to become a Christian, what did you know about a personal relationship with Jesus Christ?

_____

_____

_____

4. How did you learn or hear about how to become a Christian?

_____

_____

5. After you knew how to become a Christian, if you put off making that decision for a period of time, what were the things that caused you to put it off?

_____

_____

6. What specific thing caused you to decide to give your life to Christ?

_____

_____

2. HOW:

1. Who were you with when you made the decision to invite Christ into your life?

_____

2. Where were you when you made that decision? _____

3. When or about when in your life did you make that decision? _____

_____

4. What were the words you personally said when you prayed to become a Christian?

_____

_____

_____

_____

3. AFTER:

1. Once you invited Christ into your life, what were you aware of at that moment?

_____

_____

2. What specific needs did Jesus meet when He entered your life?

_____

_____

_____

3. What things changed in your life in the next few days, weeks, and months?

_____

_____

_____

Now, on a separate sheet of paper, using these questions and answers as a resource, write out your testimony.

We will continue working on this, so don't feel like it has to be perfect. Just write a rough draft, and we will work on it together over a period of time.

Helpful Hints for Writing Out Your Testimony

1. Speak to God first, and ask Him to speak through you.
   Ask Him to give you wisdom and guidance as you write. (JAMES 1:5,6)

2. Follow a three-point outline:
   a. Life *before* knowing Christ.
   b. *How* you came to Christ (be specific).
   c. Life *after* you received Christ (changes He has made,
      what He means to you now).

3. Begin with an interesting, attention-getting sentence and close with a good
   conclusion. Include relevant, thought-provoking, personal experiences.

4. Write in such a way that others will identify with your past and
   present experiences.

5. Give enough detail to arouse interest.

6. Use some Scripture verses.

7. Avoid —
   a. using statements which reflect negatively on people or organizations
   b. mentioning denominations
   c. preaching at people. This is a testimony, not a "preachamony".
   d. using stereotypes or overworked terms.
   e. using words that are meaningless to non-Christians, e.g. "salvation,"
      "saved," "born-again," sanctified," etc. If this type of word must be
      used, it should be clearly explained.

8. Prepare your testimony so that you can share it in a group situation
   as well as with an individual.

9. Build your testimony around a theme — something characteristic of your
   life that is of general interest to non-Christians. Examples: personal success
   (your past vs. present perspective), life goals, etc.

10. Keep in mind that your testimony should give details so that someone
    else would know how to trust Christ.

11. It is important that Christ be lifted up as the only way to eternal life
    (JOHN 14:6). Make sure this point is clearly made in your testimony.

When you have finished writing your testimony out, look in the back of this book and tear out the "TEN MOST WANTED CARD." List one or two people with whom you would eventually like to share your testimony. Begin praying regularly for those you have listed, that God would:

    1. prepare their hearts
    2. give you sensitivity to them
    3. provide an opportunity to share.

Scripture
Memory
Verse:

6 Telling Others about Christ   NIV

I PETER 3:15,16

But in your hearts set apart Christ as Lord. Always be prepared to give an answer to everyone who asks you to give the reason for the hope that you have. But do this with gentleness and respect, keeping a clear conscience, so that those who speak maliciously against your good behavior in Christ may be ashamed of their slander.

I PETER 3:15,16

NOTES

4 Assurance of Deliverance NIV

I CORINTHIANS 10:13

No temptation has seized you except what is common to man. And God is faithful; he will not let you be tempted beyond what you can bear. But when you are tempted, he will also provide a way out so that you can stand up under it.

I CORINTHIANS 10:13

5 Your Calling as an Insider NIV

I CORINTHIANS 7:24

Brothers, each man, as responsible to God, should remain in the situation God called him to.

I CORINTHIANS 7:24

6 Telling Others about Christ NIV

I PETER 3:15,16

But in your hearts set apart Christ as Lord. Always be prepared to give an answer to everyone who asks you to give the reason for the hope that you have. But do this with gentleness and respect, keeping a clear conscience, so that those who speak maliciously against your good behavior in Christ may be ashamed of their slander.

I PETER 3:15,16

1 Assurance of Salvation NIV

I JOHN 5:11-13

And this is the testimony: God has given us eternal life, and this life is in his Son. He who has the Son has life; he who does not have the Son of God does not have life. I write these things to you who believe in the name of the Son of God so that you may know that you have eternal life.

I JOHN 5:11-13

2 Fruit of the Holy Spirit NIV

GALATIANS 5:22,23

But the fruit of the Spirit is love, joy, peace, patience, kindness, goodness, faithfulness, gentleness and self-control. Against such things there is no law.

GALATIANS 5:22,23

3 The Adversary NIV

I PETER 5:8,9

Be self-controlled and alert. Your enemy the devil prowls around like a roaring lion looking for someone to devour. Resist him, standing firm in the faith, because you know that your brothers throughout the world are undergoing the same kind of sufferings.

I PETER 5:8,9

TEN MOST-WANTED

1.
2.
3.
4.
5.
6.
7.
8.
9.
10.

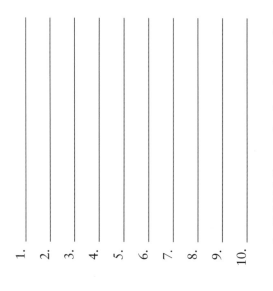

I will faithfully pray for the salvation of the above and will attempt to reach them for Christ through personal witness and other outreach efforts.

"The earnest prayer of a righteous man has great effect." JAMES 5:16

1 Assurance of Salvation KJV

I JOHN 5:11-13

And this is the record, that God hath given to us eternal life, and this life is in his Son. He that hath the Son hath life; and he that hath not the Son of God hath not life. These things have I written unto you that believe on the name of the Son of God; that ye may know that ye have eternal life, and that ye may believe on the name of the Son of God.

I JOHN 5:11-13

2 Fruit of the Holy Spirit KJV

GALATIANS 5:22,23

But the fruit of the Spirit is love, joy, peace, long-suffering, gentleness, goodness, faith, meekness, temperance: against such there is no law.

GALATIANS 5:22,23

3 The Adversary KJV

I PETER 5:8,9

Be sober, be vigilant; because your adversary the devil, as a roaring lion, walketh about, seeking whom he may devour: whom resist stedfast in the faith, knowing that the same afflictions are accomplished in your brethren that are in the world.

I PETER 5:8,9

4 Assurance of Deliverance KJV

I CORINTHIANS 10:13

There hath no temptation taken you but such as is common to man: but God is faithful, who will not suffer you to be tempted above that ye are able; but will with the temptation also make a way to escape, that ye may be able to bear it.

I CORINTHIANS 10:13

5 Your Calling as an Insider KJV

I CORINTHIANS 7:24

Brethren, let every man, wherein he is called, therein abide with God.

I CORINTHIANS 7:24

6 Telling Others about Christ KJV

I PETER 3:15,16

But sanctify the Lord God in your hearts: and be ready always to give an answer to every man that asketh you a reason of the hope that is in you with meekness and fear: Having a good conscience; that, whereas they speak evil of you, as of evildoers, they may be ashamed that falsely accuse your good conversation in Christ.

I PETER 3:15,16